Based on the best-selling keyboard method *by Kenneth Baker.*

THE COMPLETE KEYBOARD Pl

Hits 1960-197

Wise Publications
part of The Music Sales Group
London/New York/Paris/Sydney/Copenhagen/Berlin/Madrid/Tokyo

Master Chord Chart

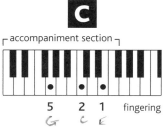

C

accompaniment section

5　2　1　fingering

G　C　E

Db(C#)

accompaniment section

4　2　1　fingering

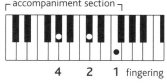

D

accompaniment section

5　3　1　fingering

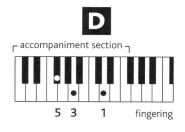

Eb(D#)

accompaniment section

5　3　1　fingering

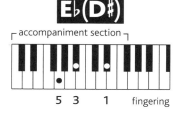

E

accompaniment section

5　3　1　fingering

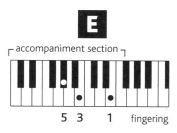

F

accompaniment section

4　2　1　fingering

A　C　F

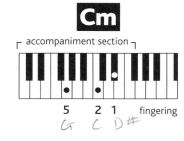

Cm

accompaniment section

5　2　1　fingering

G　C　D#

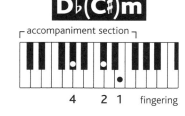

Db(C#)m

accompaniment section

4　2　1　fingering

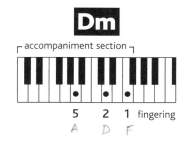

Dm

accompaniment section

5　2　1　fingering

A　D　F

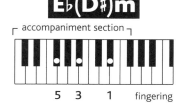

Eb(D#)m

accompaniment section

5　3　1　fingering

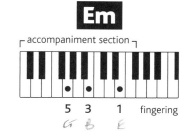

Em

accompaniment section

5　3　1　fingering

G　B　E

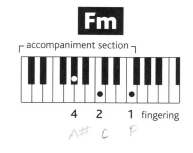

Fm

accompaniment section

4　2　1　fingering

A#　C　F

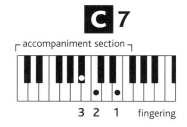

C 7

accompaniment section

3　2　1　fingering

Db(C#) 7

accompaniment section

5　3　2　1　fingering

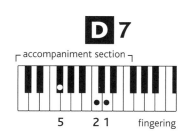

D 7

accompaniment section

5　2 1　fingering

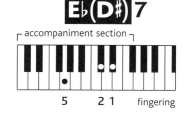

Eb(D#) 7

accompaniment section

5　2 1　fingering

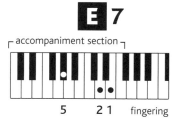

E 7

accompaniment section

5　2 1　fingering

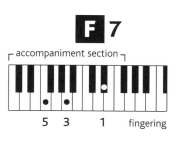

F 7

accompaniment section

5　3　1　fingering

Master Chord Chart

Gb(F#)

accompaniment section

5　　3　　1　　　fingering

Gb(F#)m

accompaniment section

5　　3　　1　　　fingering

Gb(F#)7

accompaniment section

5　　3　　1　　　fingering

G

accompaniment section

5　　3　　1　　　fingering

G　B　D

Gm

accompaniment section

5　　3　　1　　　fingering

G 7

accompaniment section

5　　3　　　1　fingering

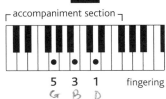

Ab(G#)

accompaniment section

4　　2　　1　　　fingering

Ab(G#)m

accompaniment section

4　　2　　1　　　fingering

Ab(G#)7

accompaniment section

5　　3　　　1 fingering

A

accompaniment section

5　　3　　1　　　fingering

Am

accompaniment section

5　3　1　　　fingering

A　C　E

A 7

accompaniment section

5　4　　2　　　fingering

Bb

accompaniment section

5　　2　1　　　fingering

Bbm

accompaniment section

5　　2　1　　　fingering

Bb 7

accompaniment section

3　2　　1　　　fingering

B

accompaniment section

5　　2　1　　　fingering

Bm

accompaniment section

5　　2　1　　　fingering

B 7

accompaniment section

4　3　　2　　　fingering

Big Spender

Words by Dorothy Fields
Music by Cy Coleman

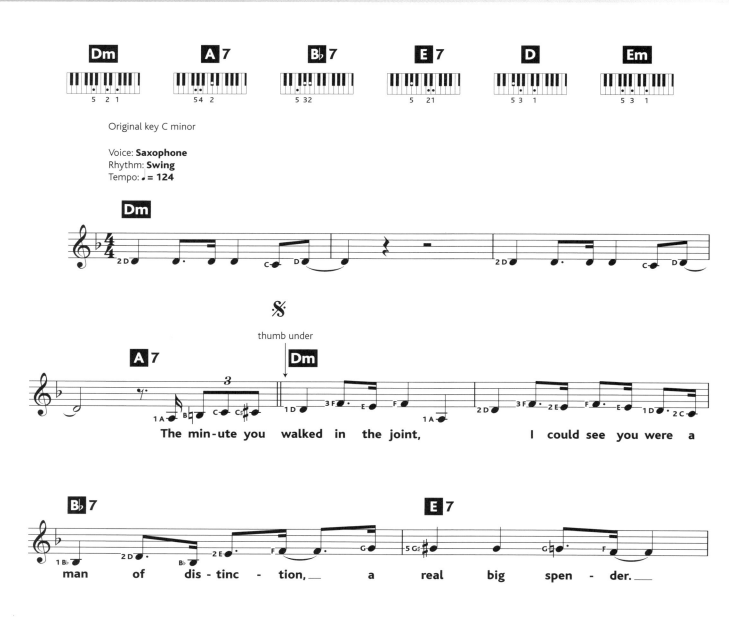

Original key C minor

Voice: **Saxophone**
Rhythm: **Swing**
Tempo: ♩ = 124

The min-ute you walked in the joint, I could see you were a

man of dis-tinc - tion, __ a real big spen - der. __

Good look - ing, __ so re - fined, __ say

would -n't you like to know what's go - ing on in my mind? So let me get

right to the point.

I don't pop my cork for

ev - 'ry man I see.____

Hey big spen - der,____

spend

a lit - tle time____ with me.____

Fine

new hand position

Would -n't you like to have

fun, fun, fun? How a-bout a few laughs, laughs.

I can show you a

good time.

Let me show you a

D.S. al Fine

good time.

The min - ute you

5

Born Free

Words by Don Black
Music by John Barry

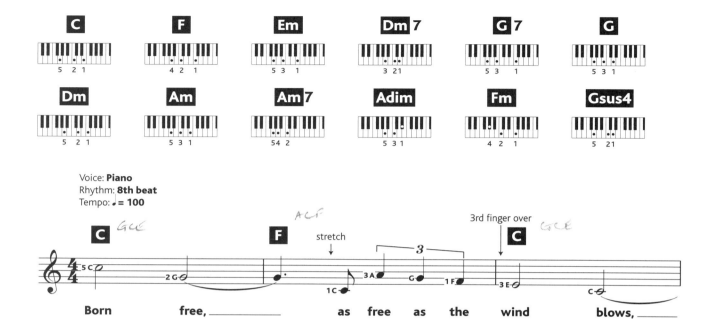

Voice: **Piano**
Rhythm: **8th beat**
Tempo: ♩ = 100

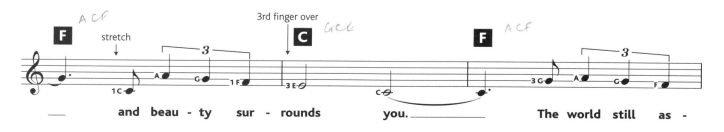

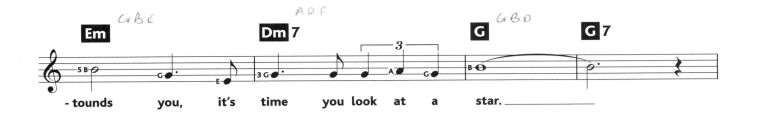

- tounds you, it's time you look at a star.

new hand position

Stay free, where no walls di - vide you,

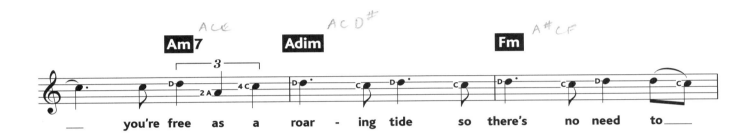

you're free as a roar - ing tide so there's no need to

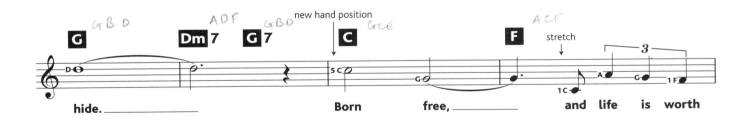

new hand position   stretch

hide. Born free, and life is worth

3rd finger over

liv - ing, but on - ly worth liv - ing 'cause

you're born free.

stop rhythm here

Baby Now That I've Found You

Words & Music by Tony Macauley & John Macleod

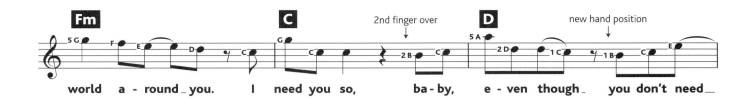

world a - round __ you. I need you so, ba - by, e - ven though __ you don't need __

__ me, you don't need __ me. __

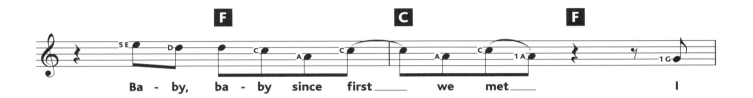

Ba - by, ba - by since first __ we met __ I

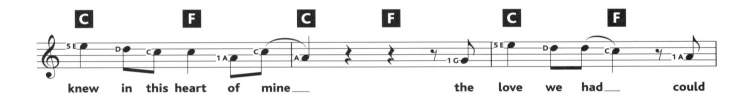

knew in this heart of mine __ the love we had __ could

not be __ bad. __ I played it right, and bide my __ time. __

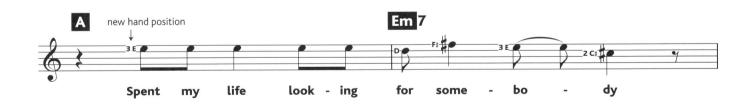

Spent my life look - ing for some - bo - dy

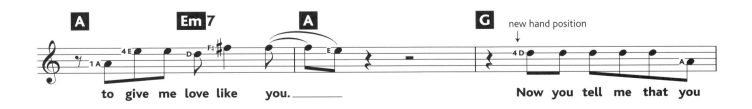

to give me love like you. Now you tell me that you

wan - na leave _ me. (Darl - in' I just can't let you.) _

Ba - by, ___ now that I've found _ you I can't let you go, built my

world a - round __ you. I need you so, ba - by,

e - ven though _ you don't need __ me, you don't need __ me. Ba - by, _

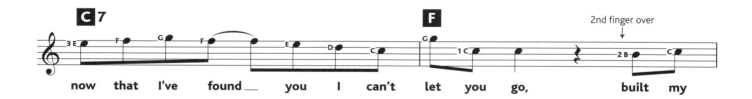

now that I've found __ you I can't let you go, built my

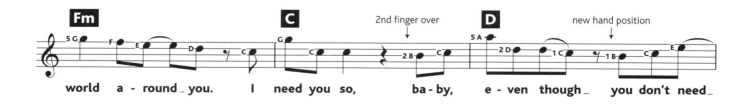

world a - round _ you. I need you so, ba - by, e - ven though _ you don't need _

_ me, you don't need __ me. _

Daydream

Words & Music by John Sebastian

Voice: **Harmonica**
Rhythm: **Swing/Shuffle**
Tempo: ♩ = 98

What a day for a day - dream, what a day for a

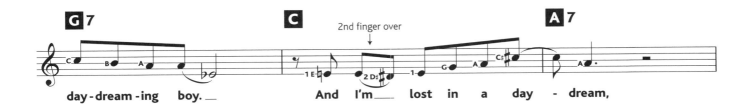

day - dream - ing boy. And I'm lost in a day - dream,

dream - ing 'bout my bun - dle of joy.

And ev - en if time ain't real - ly on my side,

it's one of those days for tak - ing a walk out - side, ___

I'm blow - ing to day to take a walk in the sun, ___

and fall on my face on some - bo - dy's new mowed lawn. ___

I've been hav - ing a sweet ___ dream, I've been dream - ing since I

woke up to - day. ___ It's star - ring me and my sweet ___ thing,

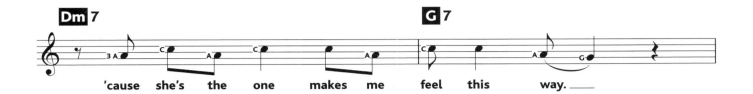

'cause she's the one makes me feel this way. ____

And ev - en if time is pass - ing me by a lot, ____

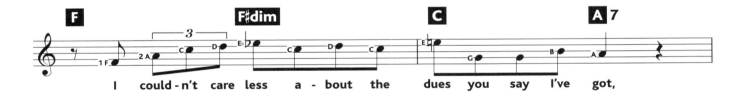

I could - n't care less a - bout the dues you say I've got,

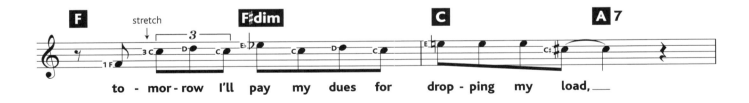

to - mor - row I'll pay my dues for drop - ping my load, ____

a pie in the face for be - ing a sleep - y bull toad. ____

California Dreamin'

Words & Music by John Phillips & Michelle Phillips

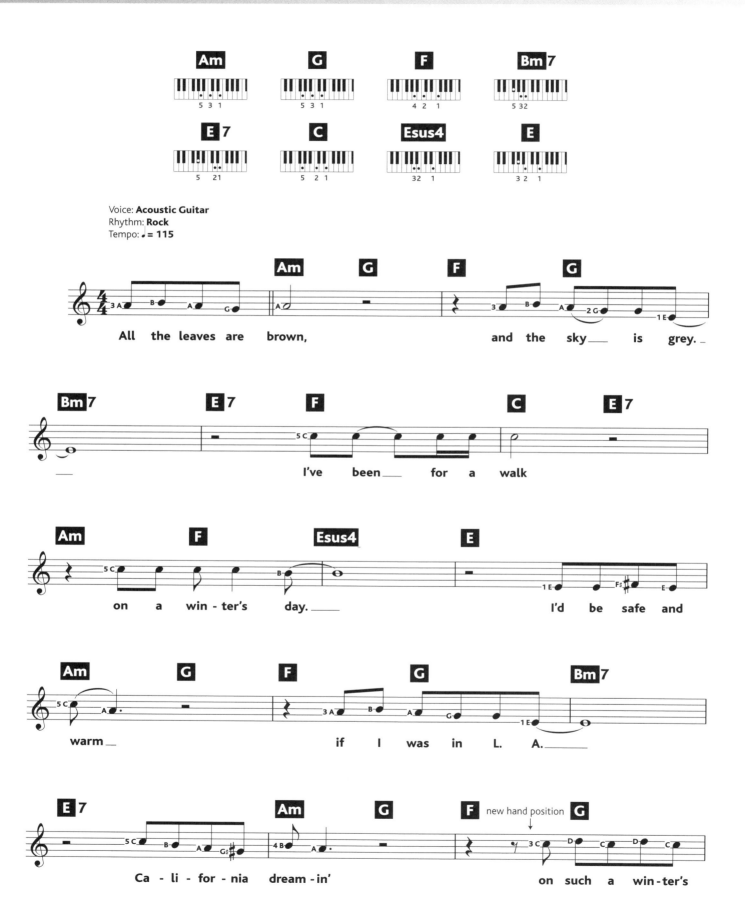

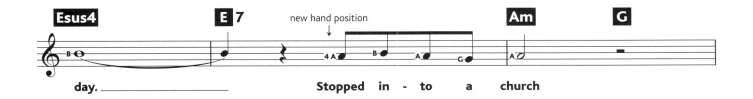

day. _____ Stopped in - to a church

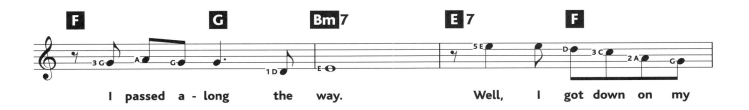

I passed a - long the way. Well, I got down on my

knees and I pre - tend____ to pray. ____

You know the preach - er liked the cold. __ He knows I'm gon - na

stay. Ca - li - for - nia dream - in'

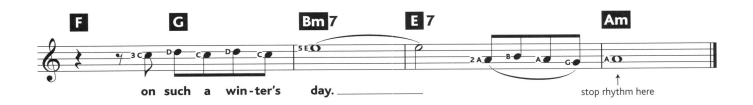

on such a win - ter's day. _____

15

Can't Take My Eyes Off You

Words & Music by Bob Crewe & Bob Gaudio

eyes off of you. _____ I love you ba - by _____ and if it's

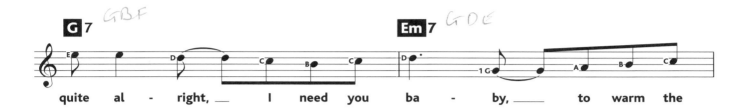

quite al - right, _____ I need you ba - by, _____ to warm the

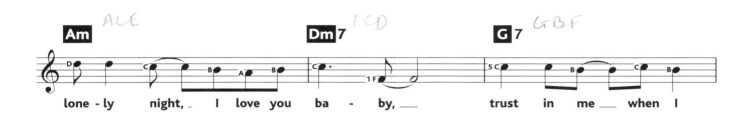

lone - ly night, _ I love you ba - by, ___ trust in me ___ when I

say, _____ oh pret - ty ba - by, _____ don't bring me

down I pray, oh pret - ty ba - by _ now that I've found you, stay _ and let me

love you, ba - by, let me love you. _____

Everybody's Talkin'

Words & Music by Fred Neil

Voice: **Flute**
Rhythm: **16th beat**
Tempo: ♩ = 120

Ev - 'ry - bo - dy's talk - in' at_____ me, I don't hear a

word they're say - in', on - ly the ech - oes_____ of my

mind._____ Peo - ple stop and stare____ and

I can't see their fa - ces,_____ on - ly the

God Only Knows

Words & Music by Brian Wilson & Tony Asher

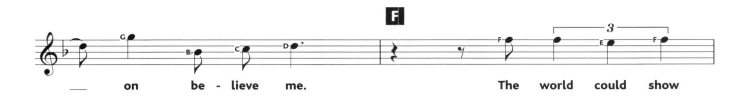

on be - lieve me. The world could show

no - thing to___ me, so what good would__ liv - ing do me?

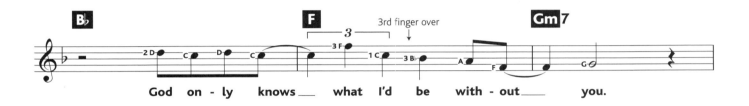

God on - ly knows ___ what I'd be with - out___ you.

God on - ly knows ___ what I'd be with - out___

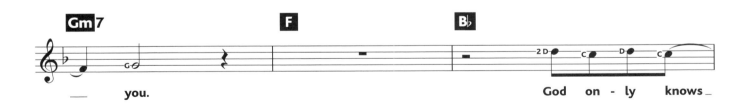

___ you. God on - ly knows __

___ what I'd be with - out___ you.

I've Gotta Get A Message To You

Words & Music by Barry Gibb, Maurice Gibb & Robin Gibb

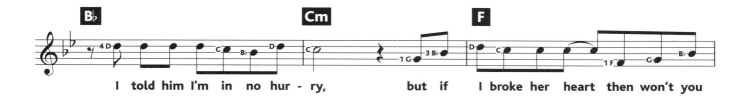

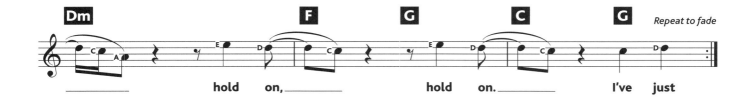

I Just Don't Know What To Do With Myself

Words by Hal David
Music by Burt Bacharach

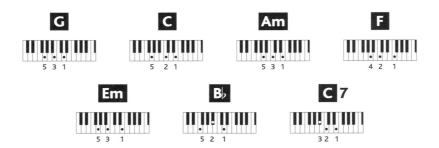

Voice: **Flute**
Rhythm: **Bossa nova**
Tempo: ♩ = 95

I just don't know what to do with my - self, don't know

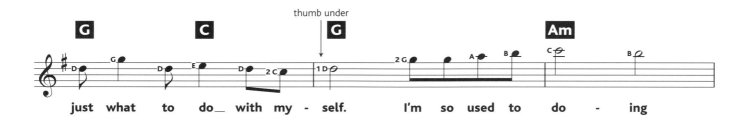

just what to do__ with my - self. I'm so used to do - ing

ev - 'ry - thing with you, plan - ning ev - 'ry - thing for two. And

now that we're through, _____ I just don't know what to do__ with my

time, I'm so lone-some for you, it's a crime. Go-ing to the

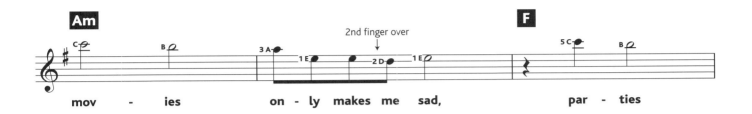

mov - ies on - ly makes me sad, par - ties

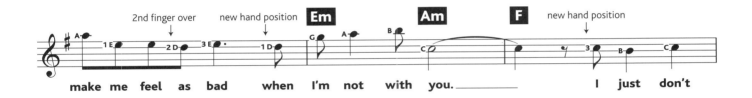

make me feel as bad when I'm not with you._____ I just don't

know what to do._____ Like a sum - mer rose,

needs the sun and rain._____ I need__ your

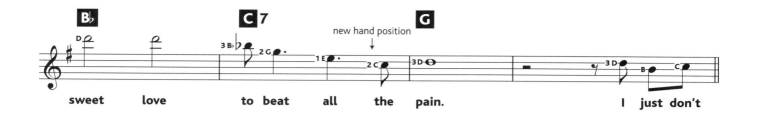

sweet   love   to beat   all   the   pain.   I just don't

know   what   to   do__ with my - self,   just don't know what   to   do   with my -

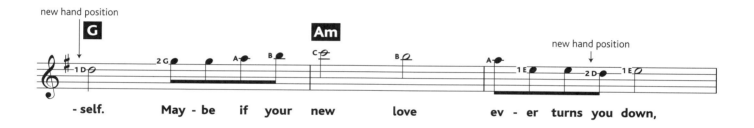

- self.   May - be   if   your   new   love   ev - er   turns   you   down,

come   back,   I   will   be   a - round   just   wait - ing   for   you.____

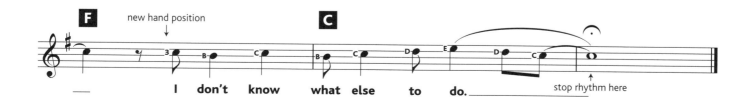

____   I   don't   know   what   else   to   do._____

Love Me Do

Words & Music by John Lennon & Paul McCartney

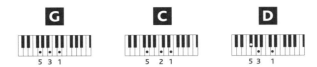

Voice: **Harmonica**
Rhythm: **Shuffle/Swing**
Tempo: ♩ = 142

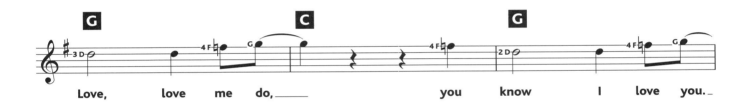

Love,   love   me   do, _____   you   know   I   love   you. _

_ ___   I'll   al - ways   be   true, _____   so

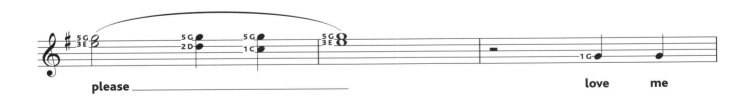

please _____   love   me

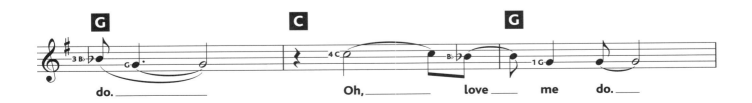

do. ____   Oh, _____   love ___   me   do. _

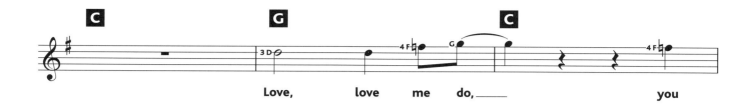

Love, love me do,＿＿ you

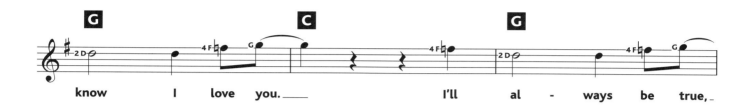

know I love you.＿＿ I'll al - ways be true,＿

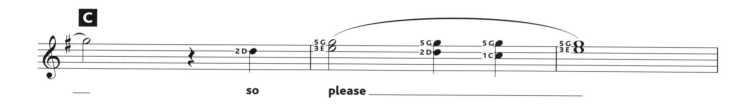

＿ so please ＿＿＿＿＿＿＿

love me do.＿＿＿＿ Oh,＿＿＿＿ love ＿

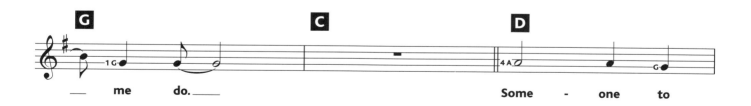

＿ me do.＿＿ Some - one to

love, some - bo - dy new.＿＿＿

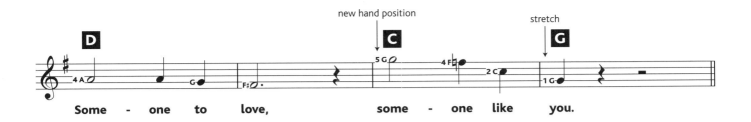

Some - one to love, some - one like you.

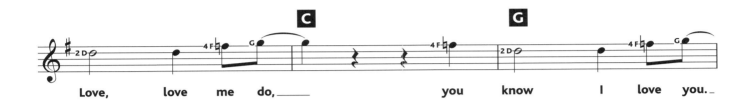

Love, love me do,_____ you know I love you.___

___ I'll al - ways be true,_____ so

please _____ love me

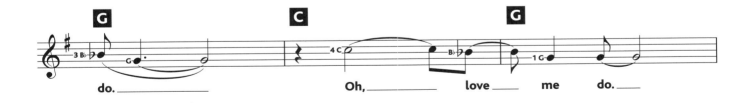

do. _____ Oh,_____ love ___ me do. ___

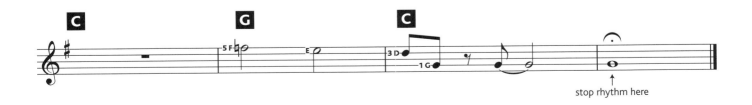

Light My Fire

Words & Music by Jim Morrison, Robbie Krieger, Ray Manzarek & John Densmore

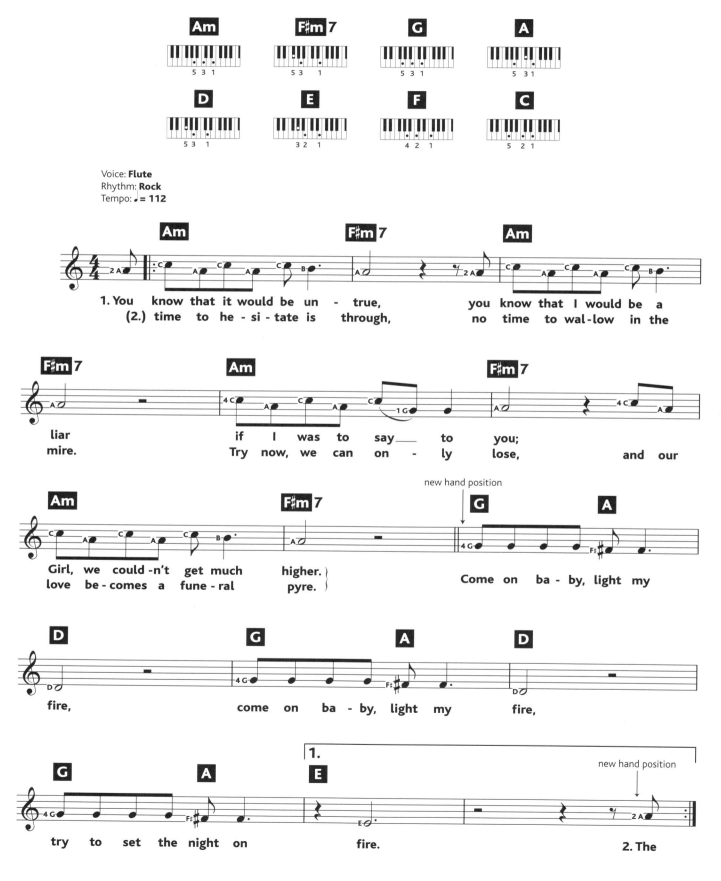

3. The time to he - si - tate is through, no

time to wal - low in the mire. Try now, we can on - ly

lose, and our love be - comes a fune - ral pyre.

new hand position

Come on ba - by, light my fire, come on ba - by, light my fire.

new hand position

Try to set the night on fire, try to set the night on

fire. Try to set the night on fire.

Only The Lonely

Words & Music by Roy Orbison & Joe Melson

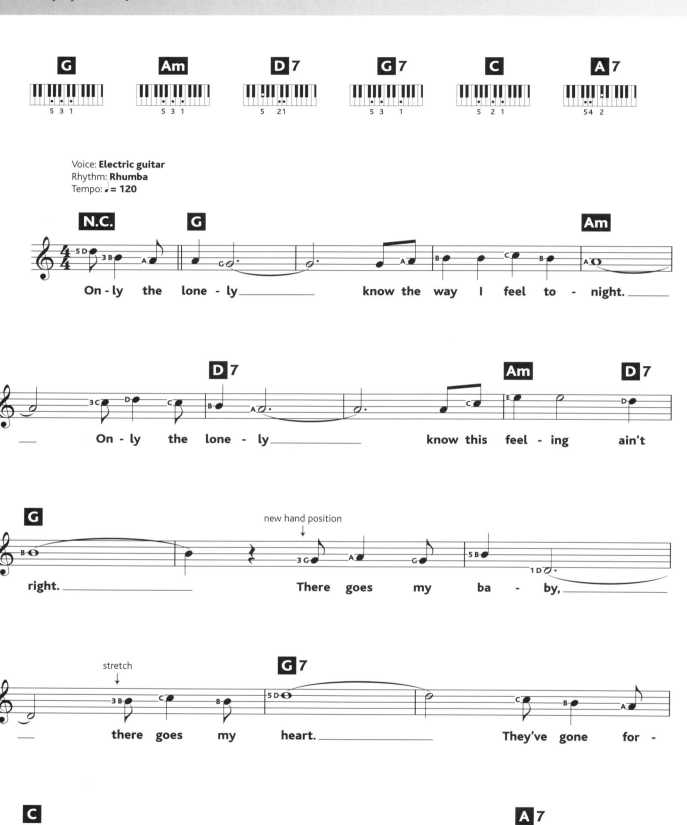

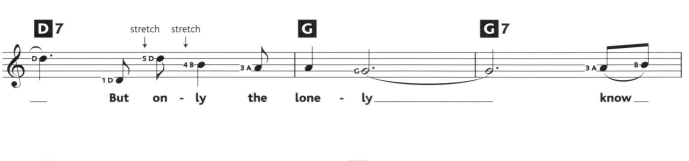

But on - ly the lone - ly _____ know _____

why _____ I cry, _____ on - ly the

lone - ly. _____ There goes my ba - by, _____ there goes my

heart. _____ They've gone for - ev - er, _____

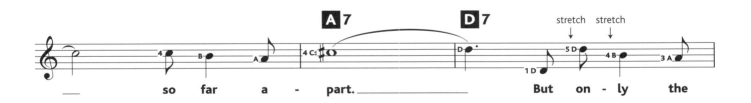

_____ so far a - part. _____ But on - ly the

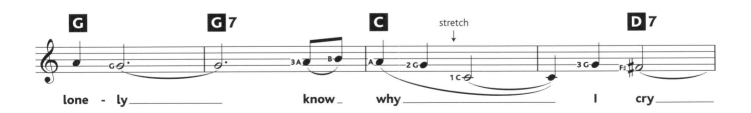

lone - ly _____ know ___ why _____ I cry _____

_____ on - ly the lone - ly. _____

Positively 4th Street

Words & Music by Bob Dylan

Nights In White Satin

Words & Music by Justin Hayward

37

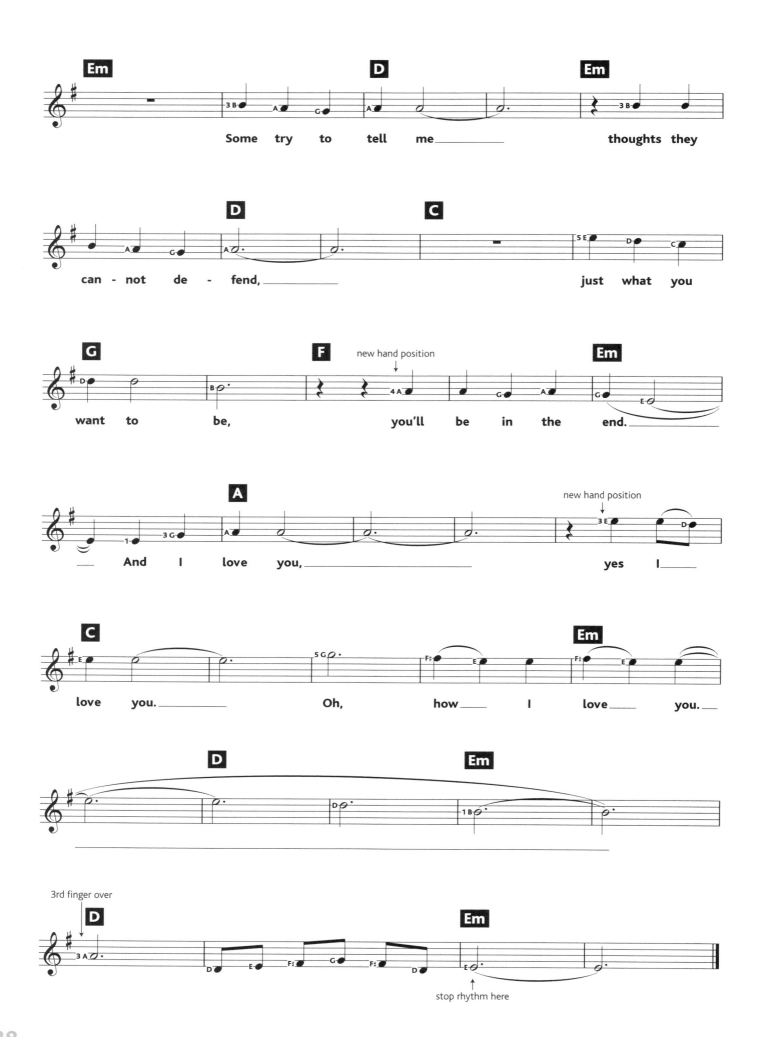

(Sittin' On) The Dock Of The Bay

Words & Music by Otis Redding & Steve Cropper

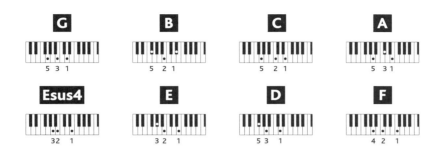

Voice: **Alto saxophone**
Rhythm: **Soul**
Tempo: ♩ = 104

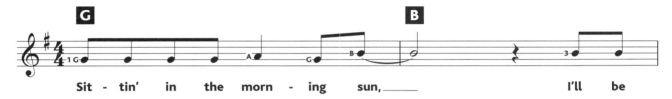

Sit - tin' in the morn - ing sun, _____ I'll be

sit - tin' when the eve - nin' _____ come. _____ Watch - in' the ships roll in, _____

_____ then I watch 'em roll a - way a - gain. _____ Yeah, _____ I'm

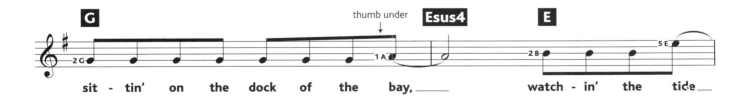

sit - tin' on the dock of the bay, _____ watch - in' the tide _____

roll _____ a - way. _____ Ooh, _____ I'm just sit - tin' on the dock of the bay, _____

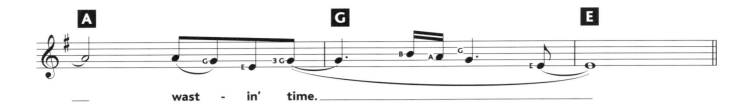

wast - in' time.

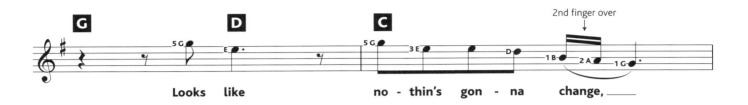

Looks like no - thin's gon - na change, _____

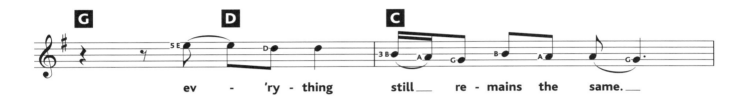

ev - 'ry - thing still ___ re - mains the same. ___

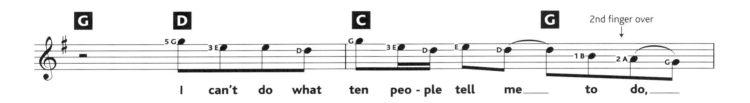

2nd finger over

I can't do what ten peo - ple tell me ___ to do, ___

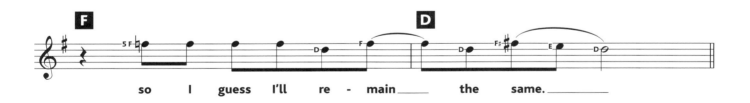

so I guess I'll re - main ___ the same. _____

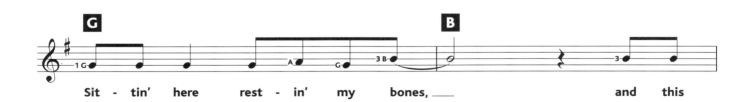

Sit - tin' here rest - in' my bones, ___ and this

lone - li - ness won't leave me a - lone. ___

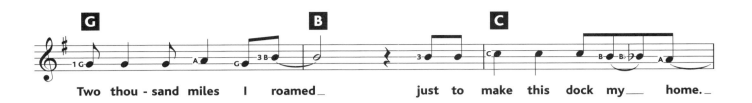

Two thou - sand miles I roamed just to make this dock my home.

Now, I'm just sit - tin' at the dock of the bay, watch - in' the tide

roll a - way. Ooh, I'm just sit - tin' on the dock of the bay,

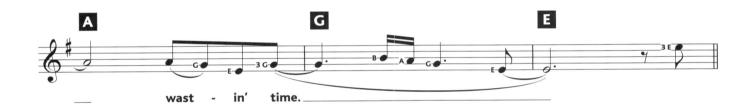

wast - in' time.

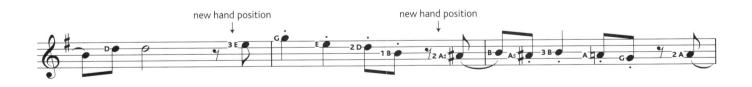

41

The Sound Of Silence

Words & Music by Paul Simon

si - lence. _____ In rest - less dreams I walked a -

- lone, nar - row streets of cob - ble - stone,

new hand position

'neath the ha - lo of a street - lamp. _____

I turned my col - lar to the cold and damp, _____

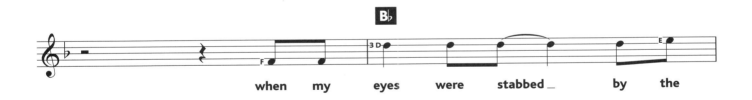

when my eyes were stabbed _____ by the

flash of a ne - on light that split the night _____

new hand position   new hand position

_____ and touched the sound of si - lence. _____

Stand By Me

Words & Music by Ben E. King, Jerry Leiber & Mike Stoller

Voice: **Saxophone**
Rhythm: **Soft rock/Rhumba**
Tempo: ♩ = 118

When the night has come, and the land is

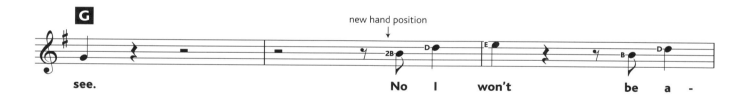

dark, and the moon ____ is the on - ly light we'll

see. No I won't be a -

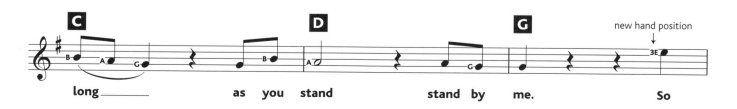

- fraid, I ____ won't be a - fraid, just as

long ____ as you stand stand by me. So

darl - ing, darl - ing, stand by me, Oh____

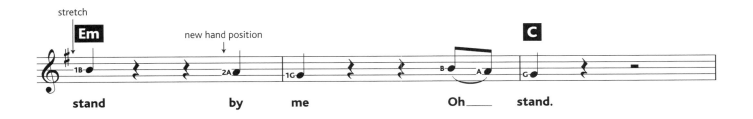

stand by me Oh____ stand.

Stand by me, stand by me. So darl - ing, darl - ing,

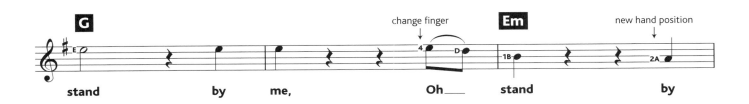

stand by me, Oh____ stand by

me Oh____ stand. Stand by me,

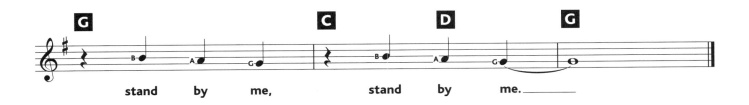

stand by me, stand by me.____

Strangers In The Night

Words by Charles Singleton & Eddie Snyder
Music by Bert Kaempfert

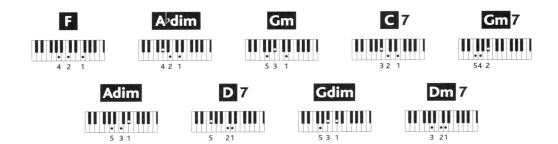

Voice: **Clarinet**
Rhythm: **Latin**
Tempo: ♩ = 90

Stran - gers in the night _____ ex - chang - ing glan - ces,

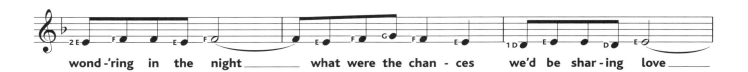

wond -'ring in the night _____ what were the chan - ces we'd be shar - ing love _____

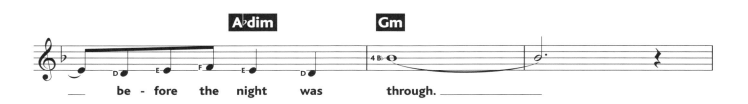

_____ be - fore the night was through. _____

new hand position

Some - thing in your eyes _____ was so in - vit - ing,

some - thing in your smile _____ was so ex - cit - ing,

some -thing in my heart _____ told me I must have you. _____

_____ Stran -gers in the night, _____ two lone - ly peo - ple we were

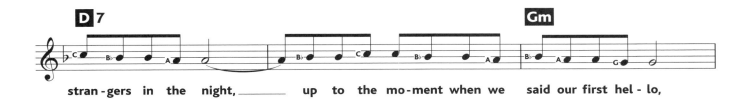

stran -gers in the night, _____ up to the mo -ment when we said our first hel - lo,

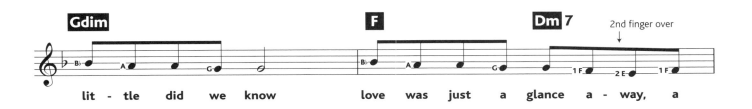

2nd finger over

lit - tle did we know love was just a glance a - way, a

warm em -brac -ing dance a - way. And ev - er since that night _____ we've been to - ge - ther

lov - ers at first sight, _____ in love for ev - er, it turned out so right _____

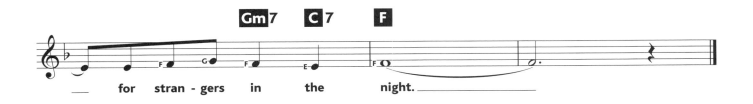

_____ for stran - gers in the night. _____

Streets Of London

Words & Music by Ralph McTell

Original key E major

Voice: **String ensemble**
Rhythm: **Bossa nova**
Tempo: ♩ = 148

yes - ter - day's news._____ So

how can you tell me you're lone - -

- ly, and say for you that the sun don't

shine?_____ Let me take you

by the hand and lead you through the streets of Lon - don,

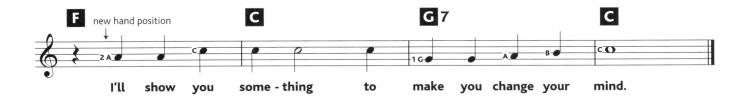

I'll show you some - thing to make you change your mind.

Suspicious Minds

Words & Music by Francis Zambon

Voice: **Clarinet**
Rhythm: **Pop**
Tempo: ♩ = 110

We're caught in a trap, ___ I can't walk out, ___ be-cause I love ___ you too ___ much ba- -by. ___ Why can't you see ___ what you're do-ing to me, ___ when you don't be - lieve ___ a word I say? ___

We can't go on___ to - ge - ther ___

with sus - pi - cious ___ minds. ___ (Sus - pi - cious ___ minds.) _

__ And we can't build ___ our dreams _ on sus - pi - cious

minds. _____ We're caught in a trap, ___

I can't walk out, ___ be - cause I love _

__ you too ___ much ba - by. ___

These Boots Are Made For Walkin'

Words & Music by Lee Hazlewood

One of these days these boots are gon - na walk all ov - er you.

You keep say - in' you got some - thin' for me.

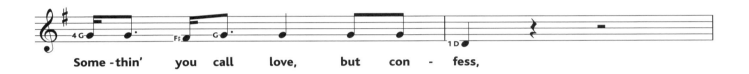

Some - thin' you call love, but con - fess,

you been a - mess - in' where you shoudn't have been a mess - in'. And now

some - one else is get - tin' all your best. These

boots are made for walk - in' and that's just what they'll do.

One of these days these boots are gon - na walk all ov - er you.

Walk Away, Renee

Words & Music by Bob Calilli, Tony Sansome & Michael Lookofsky

Voice: **Piano**
Rhythm: **Pop**
Tempo: ♩ = 116

And when I see ____ the sign ____ that points one way, ____
From deep in - side ____ the tears ____ that I forced to cry, ____

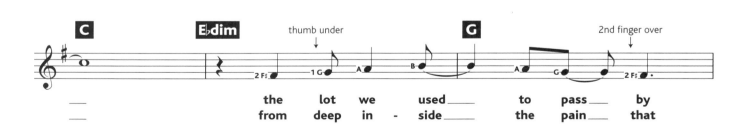

____ the lot we used ____ to pass ____ by
____ from deep in - side ____ the pain ____ that

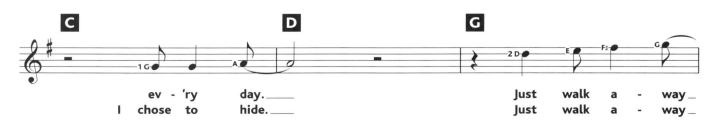

ev - 'ry day. ____   Just walk a - way ____
I chose to hide. ____   Just walk a - way ____

Em   C   G   2nd finger over   D

__ Re - nee, _____ you won't see me fol - low you back home.
__ Re - nee, _____ you won't see me fol - low you back home.

G   Em   C   3rd finger over

The emp - ty side__ walks on__ my block__ are not the same;__
Now as the rain__ beats down_ up - on__ my wea - ry eyes,__

G   C   Am7   G   D

_____ you're not to blame. __
_____ for me it cries. __

G   Em   C

Just walk a - way__ Re - nee,_____ you won't see me fol - low

G   2nd finger over   D   G   Em

you back home.   Now as the rain__ beats down_ up - on__

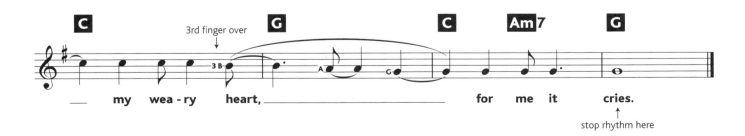

C   3rd finger over   G   C   Am7   G

__ my wea - ry heart,_____ for me it cries.

stop rhythm here

A Whiter Shade Of Pale

Words by Keith Reid
Music by Matthew Fisher & Gary Brooker

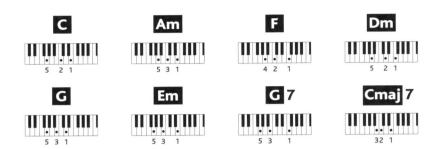

more.   The room was hum - ming hard - er

as the ceil - ing flew a - way. ___

When we called out for an - oth - er drink

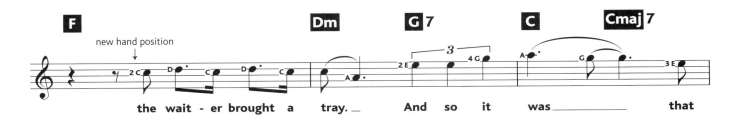

the wait - er brought a tray. ___ And so it was ___ that

lat - er   as the mill - er told his tale ___

that her face, at first just ghost - ly,   turned a

whit - er ___ shade of pale. ___

What A Wonderful World

Words & Music by George Weiss & Bob Thiele

58

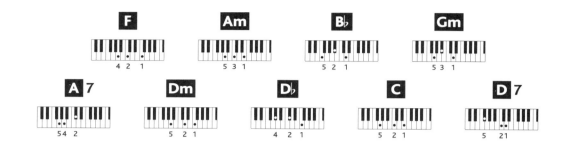

Voice: **Clarinet**
Rhythm: **Swing**
Tempo: **Gently** ♩ = 72

I see trees of green, __ red __ ro - ses too,

I see them bloom for me and you. And I

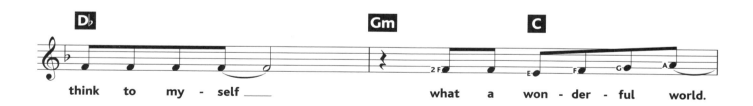

think to my - self __ what a won - der - ful world.

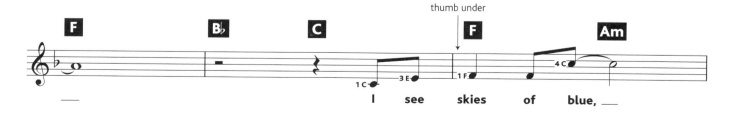

I see skies of blue, __

and clouds of white, the bright bless - ed day,

the dark sa - cred night, and I think to my - self, ___

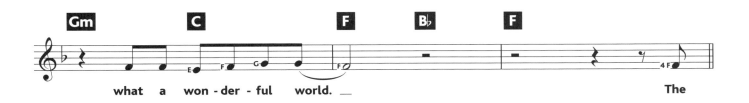

what a won - der - ful world. ___ The

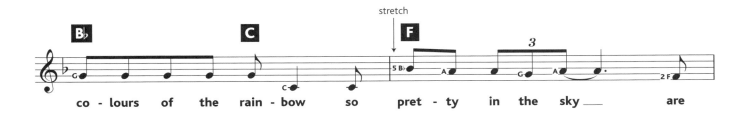

co - lours of the rain - bow so pret - ty in the sky ___ are

al - so on the fa - ces of peo - ple go - ing by. I see

friends shak - ing hands, say - ing "How do you do?" ___

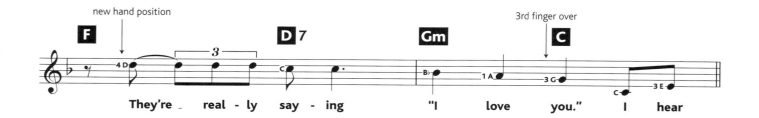

They're _ real - ly say - ing "I love you." I hear

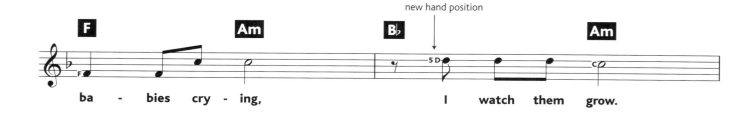

ba - bies cry - ing, I watch them grow.

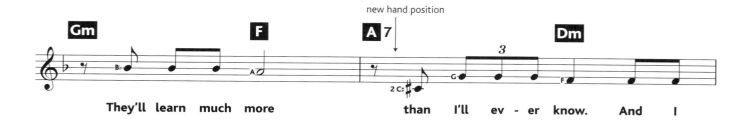

They'll learn much more than I'll ev - er know. And I

think to my - self, ___ what a won - der - ful world. ___

Yes I think to my - self, ___

what a won - der - ful world.

You Really Got Me

Words & Music by Ray Davies

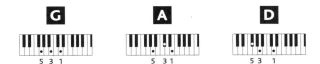

Voice: **Electric Guitar**
Rhythm: **Rock**
Tempo: ♩ = 130

Girl, you real - ly got me go - ing, you got me

so I don't know what I'm do - ing now.

Yeah, you real - ly got me now, you got me

new hand position

so I can't sleep at night. Yeah, you real - ly

got me now,   you got me so   I don't what what I'm do - ing___

D

___ now.   Oh   yeah,   you real - ly   got me now,   you got me

so   I   can't sleep   at night,   you   real - ly   got   me,___   you

new hand position

real - ly   got   me,___   you   real - ly   got   me.___

G

See,   don't ev - er   set   me   free, ___   I   al - ways

want   to   be   by   your   side. _____   Girl,   you   real - ly

got me now, you got me so I can't sleep at night.

new hand position

A

Yeah, you real - ly got me now, you got me

so I don't know what I'm do - ing now. Oh

D

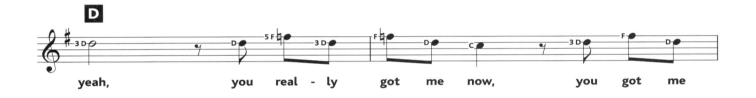

yeah, you real - ly got me now, you got me

so I can't sleep at night. You real - ly got me, you

new hand position

real - ly got me, you real - ly got me.

G

Published by
Wise Publications
14-15 Berners Street, London W1T 3LJ, UK.

Exclusive Distributors:
Music Sales Limited
Distribution Centre, Newmarket Road,
Bury St Edmunds, Suffolk IP33 3YB, UK.
Music Sales Pty Limited
120 Rothschild Avenue, Rosebery, NSW 2018, Australia.

This book © Copyright 2008 Wise Publications,
a division of Music Sales Limited.
Order No. AM993652
ISBN 978-1-84772-561-5

Edited by Sam Harrop.
Music arranged by Paul Honey.
Music processed by Paul Ewers Music Design.
Printed in the EU.

Your Guarantee of Quality
As publishers, we strive to produce every book
to the highest commercial standards.
This book has been carefully designed to minimise awkward
page turns and to make playing from it a real pleasure.
Particular care has been given to specifying acid-free, neutral-sized paper
made from pulps which have not been elemental chlorine bleached.
This pulp is from farmed sustainable forests and was produced with special
regard for the environment. Throughout, the printing and binding have been
planned to ensure a sturdy, attractive publication which should give years of enjoyment.
If your copy fails to meet our high standards, please inform us and
we will gladly replace it.

www.musicsales.com